Redwall
Friend and Foe

BRIAN JACQUES

Tales of
Redwall
•Martin the Warrior
•Mossflower
• The Legend of Luke
•Outcast of Redwall
•Mariel of Redwall
•The Bellmaker
•Salamandastron
•Redwall
•Mattimeo
•The Pearls of Lutra
• The Long Patrol
• Marlfox

Red Fox
Published by Random House Children's Books
20 Vauxhall Bridge Road, London SW1V 2SA
A division of The Random House Group Ltd
London Melbourne Sydney Auckland
Johannesburg and agencies throughout the world
Copyright © Illustrations Chris Baker 2000
Copyright © Introduction and story text Brian Jacques 2000
Copyright © text and layout Random House Children's Books 2000
Edited by Helen Mackenzie Smith
1 3 5 7 9 10 8 6 4 2
First published in Great Britain by Red Fox 2000
All rights reserved
Printed in Hong Kong
THE RANDOM HOUSE GROUP Limited Reg. No. 954009
ISBN 0 09 926425 0

Redwall
Friend and Foe

INTRODUCTION

I like my baddies to be totally wicked and my goodies to be heroically on the side of right! From my very first villain, Cluny the Scourge, I have imbued my wicked baddies with certain characteristics. They must be vermin: rat, stoat, ferret, weasel, fox, wildcat or pine marten. These leaders of hordes are invariably stronger and more ruthless than their followers, in whom they instil obedience by fear. An arch villain always lusts after power, wants to conquer everything and rule all. He, or she, has no sympathy for any living creature that stands in the way of their malicious ambitions.

Cluny, Slagar and Gabool were typical baddies; repellent, ugly and usually insane. Ferahgo the Assassin, however, was a departure from the norm. He was very handsome, and his bright blue eyes smiled a lot, even when he was stabbing another creature in the back. Ublaz Mad Eyes was another such chieftain; sly and lethal. This was to illustrate to my young readers that somebody bad is not necessarily an ugly or deformed person; evil has some very personable faces.

I always try to make my villains' names sound harsh, or silkily sinister: Urgan Nagru and Malkariss, for example. Tsarmina was the title of the old Russian Queen, Tsarina. I wanted it to sound bad, so I put a bit of mean in the middle!

These are the villains who threaten Redwall Abbey. I hope you hate them as much as you admire my heroes.

Martin the Warrior is the role model for all my Redwall Abbey goodies - he is the ultimate hero. A tough kid who has learned to hate evil the hard way, under a slave driver's lash. Martin's life is touched by sadness and tragedy; the loss of his parents, and Rose, the great love of his life. But does he sit about moping all the time? 'Bo urr, ee'm surpintly duzz not, zurr!!' (To quote Foremole.)

Like Martin, my heroes and heroines are all young creatures, the same as the young people who read my books. The lesson is this: you must learn to be a warrior. This does not mean being a martial arts expert or a Hollywood movie star. The warrior is someone whom others look to. One who tells the truth, defends the weak and is trustworthy and courageous. In short, somebody who is true to his or her friends and family.

Whereas Martin started off tough, Matthias was a bumbling little orphan who learned to become a warrior when his beloved Abbey was threatened. Mattimeo started out as the warrior's son, slightly spoiled with little to worry about until he and his pals were taken as slaves. Then he, too, learned how to become a warrior hero. But, as I always say, not through any magic tricks. No, my warriors gain heroic stature by their own determination.

If you admire a real heroine, then take a look at my first warrioress, Mariel. Now there was a feisty young battler I enjoyed creating and writing about. Lots of girls tell me they admire Mariel greatly.

Finally, my fated heroes, the Rulers and Badger Lords of Salamandastron: Boar, Urthstripe, Sunflash and Cregga Rose Eyes. The fated ones, who in battle become possessed by the Bloodwrath. These are my legendary beasts laden with destiny, knowing no fear and fearing no vermin.

Heroes are born, maybe not knowing that they are great warriors, until the spark of courage within them is ignited to flame. As with the villains, I repeat my message. There is no such thing as wickedness or evil in a hero. Goodies are GOOD!

Redwall's Heroes ❖

Not every creature, no matter how hard they try, will become one of Redwall's legendary warriors. The characters featured in this section are those who have found the wisdom, honour and courage deep within themselves to reserve their place in Redwall history.

MARTIN THE WARRIOR
Appears in: *Martin the Warrior, Mossflower* and *The Legend of Luke*

Martin is the embodiment of Redwall's spirit. Throughout his lifetime he fights for good against evil. Even after his death, he remains with the creatures of the Abbey in their dreams, guarding their present and looking out for their future.

Martin is a born warrior and the son of Luke, from whom he inherited his famous sword. Even those adversaries who cross his path are grudgingly forced to acknowledge the noble qualities that radiate from him.

In *Martin the Warrior*, Martin fights the evil stoat Badrang the Tyrant, rallying an army against him and liberating the slaves of Marshank. It is not long before he is called again to battle on behalf of the innocent, as he takes on Tsarmina the Wildcat, oppressor of kind, honest creatures, in *Mossflower*. Once again, Martin triumphs and goes on to found Redwall Abbey.

LUKE THE WARRIOR
Appears in: *The Legend of Luke*

When his beloved wife is murdered by the pirate stoat Vilu Daskar, Luke vows vengeance - a life for a life. He pursues Daskar's ship, *Goreleech*, across the high seas and finally comes face to face with his enemy when Daskar destroys Luke's ship and takes the survivors as slaves. On the pretence of leading his captor to hidden treasure, Luke steers *Goreleech*

onto the rocks, where she is wrecked. Dying in order to fulfil his promise, Luke makes the ultimate sacrifice to rid land and sea of Daskar's evil presence.

SUNFLASH THE MACE
Appears in: *Outcast of Redwall*

As a young badger, Sunflash is captured and tortured by the ferret Swartt Sixclaw. On his escape he vows that one day he

will have his revenge. At the same time, the badger has strange dreams of a mountain fortress. These two strands of Sunflash's life become interwoven when he finally comes to Salamandastron to fulfil his destiny as a Badger Lord and to destroy his old enemy, Sixclaw.

MARIEL OF REDWALL
Appears in: *Mariel of Redwall, The Bellmaker*

Fiercely independent, young mousemaid Mariel is a survivor and a warrior. Thrown from a cliff by searat Gabool the Wild, Mariel manages to survive and makes her way to Redwall. At the Abbey she meets Dandin. Together with him and several new friends, she returns to Terramort to kill Gabool and rescue her father, Joseph the Bellmaker.

JOSEPH THE BELLMAKER
Appears in: *Mariel of Redwall, The Bellmaker*

Visited in a dream by Martin the Warrior, Joseph is instructed to journey to Southsward where Mariel and Dandin need his help. With their royal family imprisoned and their castle overrun by the foxes Urgan Nagru and Silvamord, the creatures of Southsward are in a desperate situation. But with his chosen friends, Joseph comes to their aid and helps the inhabitants to regain their independence.

URTHSTRIPE THE STRONG
Appears in: *Salamandastron*

Orphaned as a babe, Urthstripe the Strong is Badger Lord of Salamandastron. When the mountain fortress comes under attack from Ferahgo the Assassin, Urthstripe is disturbed by a sense of the familiar about his opponent - explained by the fact that Ferahgo murdered Urthstripe's parents. A fierce warrior of huge strength coupled with surprising agility, Urthstripe gives up his life in defence of Salamandastron and his twin brother, Urthwyte, with whom he is not reunited until it is tragically too late.

MATTHIAS
Appears in: *Redwall, Mattimeo*

A clumsy young mouse at the beginning of *Redwall*, Matthias is a courageous and accomplished warrior by its end. His experiences teach him

to follow in the footsteps of the legendary Martin, whom he is said to resemble closely. Matthias uses a combination of intelligence and strength to track down the sword of Martin the Warrior, retrieve it from the terrible snake, Asmodeus, and restore it to its rightful owners. At the same time, he also manages to defeat Cluny the Scourge and ensure that the Abbey remains a peaceful sanctuary for future generations.

MATTIMEO
Appears in: *Mattimeo*

Mattimeo, like his father, Matthias, takes on the spirit of a warrior when the survival of those around him depends upon his doing so. Before his experiences at the paw of Slagar the Cruel, Mattimeo is spoilt and headstrong. By the time he comes to fight side by side with his father in the Kingdom of Malkariss, however, he has become a fully fledged warrior, able to take over from Matthias as Abbey Champion.

GRATH LONGFLETCH
Appears in: *The Pearls of Lutra*

When her entire family is slain by the troops of Emperor Ublaz for the sake of six pearls, Grath vows vengeance on the pine marten and will not rest until she has it. With the help of the Redwallers, whose Abbot has been taken hostage by Ublaz, Grath is able to achieve her goal. She eventually finds happiness with Inbar Trueflight and returns with him to live at Holt Rudderwake.

TAMMO
Appears in: *The Long Patrol*

Tammo is desperate to join the famous Long
Patrol like his parents before him,
but his father claims he is too
young and undisciplined. With
the warrior training he receives
from the squirrel Russa Nodrey,
however, he is able to fulfil his
dream. Together with the other hares,
Tammo goes to Redwall to warn the
Abbey-dwellers of the presence of the evil
Damug Warfang and his army in Mossflower. When the
time comes, Tammo proves himself as a warrior and
is truly worthy of his place as a captain of the
Long Patrol.

DANNFLOR REGUBA
Appears in: *Marlfox*

Dann, a young squirrel, is put under constant
pressure by his father, Rusvul, to live up
to the honour of his family name. But
when Marlfox break into Redwall
and steal the famed tapestry during
Dann's watch, Rusvul brands his son
a coward. Dann leaves Redwall on
a mission to retrieve the tapestry
and prove himself worthy of his father's
praise. He fulfils his promise and is
made Champion of Redwall on
his return.

For every Redwall hero there is a villain. Without scruples or honour, and motivated by greed and cruelty, these villainous vermin threaten the freedom and peace of honest creatures. But they must learn that the way of a villain can only end in defeat.

BADRANG THE TYRANT
Appears in: *Martin the Warrior*

The battle-hardened stoat, Badrang the Tyrant, is vicious and ruthless, letting nothing get in the way of his ambition to become Lord of all the Eastern Coast. He presides over his fortress, Marshank, in a reign of terror. But his false power, created by bullying and torture, utterly deserts him when he comes face to face with young Martin the Warrior in the final battle.

TSARMINA THE WILDCAT
Appears in: *Mossflower*

Tsarmina is the headstrong daughter of Lord Verdauga Greeneyes, but shows little regard for family ties when she plots to have her father killed and then frames her brother for the crime. Tsarmina assumes total control over the fortress, Kotir, and exerts her tyrannical will over the woodlanders of Mossflower. Despite her power, Tsarmina is haunted by nightmares of water, foreseeing her watery death as she flees for her life from the mighty Martin.

VILU DASKAR
Appears in: *The Legend of Luke*

The pirate stoat, Vilu Daskar, captain of the *Goreleech*, plunders and kills without conscience. With slaves forced to row his ship, Daskar roams the high seas in search of treasure, casually disposing of those who get in his way. He is sly, cruel, unpredictable and, in his own words, does his best to be the worst. But when the *Goreleech* and its villainous crew attack the tribe of Luke the Warrior, Daskar makes a fatal mistake and a formidable enemy who will ensure that his ship becomes his grave.

SWARTT SIXCLAW
Appears in: *Outcast of Redwall*

An evil ferret with a sixclawed paw, Swartt Sixclaw takes great pleasure in causing torment and pain. When Sunflash, the young badger whom he has taken prisoner, permanently damages this trademark claw during his escape, Sixclaw vows to hunt him down and kill him slowly. This he attempts to do, leaving a trail of poison and death behind him. But when he reaches the mountain fortress of Salamandastron, Sixclaw proves that he is ultimately no match for Sunflash.

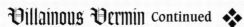

GABOOL THE WILD
Appears in: *Mariel of Redwall*

Gabool the Wild, King of the Searats, is the fiercest fighter alive and destroys those who dare to cross him. Having captured Mariel and Joseph the Bellmaker, together with the great bell, Gabool disposes of his prisoners and keeps the bell. But he is haunted by awful nightmares of fearsome badgers, avenging mice and a bell that sounds without being touched. Rapidly driven out of his mind, Gabool's nightmares become terrible reality and he is ultimately killed by his own secret weapon - the scorpion, Skrabblag.

URGAN NAGRU
Appears in: *The Bellmaker*

Together with his mate, Silvamord, the fox Urgan Nagru commands a horde of savage grey rats. Driven from the northlands by the bitter cold they come to Southsward to plunder and destroy. But the fox has not reckoned on the determination of the Southswarders who, led by Mariel, Dandin and other brave creatures, form an army to regain their freedom. Revealed as a fraud (the wolf he claims to have killed is said by Silvamord to have frozen to death), Urgan Nagru perishes in battle against the brave sea otter, Finnbarr Galedeep.

FERAHGO THE ASSASSIN
Appears in: *Salamandastron*

An evil and pitiless weasel, Ferahgo the Assassin's pale blue eyes and seemingly friendly smile conceal the depth of villainy to which he is able to sink. Having killed the parents of Urthstripe and Urthwyte, Ferahgo leaves the two badger babes to die - a mistake that is to prove fatal when he later goes in search of the rumoured treasure of Salamandastron, where Urthstripe is Badger Lord. Dismissing badgers as fierce fighters who lack cunning and are hampered by conscience, Ferahgo underestimates his opponent at the expense of his life.

CLUNY THE SCOURGE
Appears in: *Redwall*

The name, Cluny the Scourge is known and feared throughout Mossflower. And when the evil rat appears in the peaceful area, it looks as though those fears are justified. Cluny covets Redwall Abbey and plans to have it for himself, renaming it Cluny Castle and taking the Redwallers and woodlanders as  his slaves. Despite his grand intentions, Cluny is nagged by persistent nightmares in which he is killed by a warrior mouse. When Matthias appears, looking identical to the image of Martin the Warrior in the famous tapestry, Cluny's nightmares become all too real.

SLAGAR THE CRUEL
Appears in: *Mattimeo*

Following an attack by
the adder Asmodeus
(for which he falsely
holds the Redwallers
responsible), Slagar the
fox is forced to wear a
hood to disguise his
hideous injuries. Driven
by a desire for revenge
upon the Redwallers, he kidnaps five of their young,
including Mattimeo, and takes them to be used as slaves in
the underground kingdom of Malkariss. Greedy and
ambitious, Slagar plans to control the kingdom himself one
day. But, trying to escape from Matthias and Orlando the
Axe, he falls into an old well (the secret exit from the
kingdom) and plummets to his death.

EMPEROR UBLAZ
Appears in: *The Pearls of Lutra*

Also known as Mad Eyes for
his intense, hypnotic stare,
Emperor Ublaz is the cunning
ruler of the Isle of Sampetra.
With his army of trident-
bearing rats and the terrifying
Monitor Lizards, he ensures
that by controlling the timber
needed for ships, no creature is
able to leave without his
permission. When the Tears of all Oceans, the pearls that
he covets, are stolen, Ublaz swears revenge. Instead of
regaining the pearls, however, the tyrant is defeated by
Grath Longfletch and Martin of Redwall.

DAMUG WARFANG

Appears in: *The Long Patrol*

A Greatrat, Damug Warfang kills his own brother in a battle to determine who will succeed their father as Firstblade of all Rapscallions. Victorious through cheating, he takes control of the vermin horde and leads them on a mission to plunder inland. When he hears about the vulnerability of Redwall's collapsing south wall, Damug Warfang decides to conquer the Abbey. But he has not taken into account the determination of the Redwallers to retain their freedom!

MOKKAN

Appears in: *Marlfox*

Highly intelligent, and a master of the Marlfox arts of stealth and deceit, Mokkan is widely acknowledged to be the most evil of all the Marlfox. Constantly scheming and plotting, he is a natural survivor ... until the Marlfox make the mistake of stealing Redwall's famous tapestry. Back at

Castle Marl with the prize, Mokkan declares himself king, only to be troubled by nightmares. The embodiment of the horrors that torment him arrives in the form of Dann, Song and their companions, intent on taking back the tapestry and ridding the world of the Marlfox forever.

As well as the brothers and sisters of Redwall's peaceful order of mice, there are many other creatures who have a vital role to play in the Abbey's continued safety and prosperity. As Martin the Warrior advises Tansy: 'Never forget that friendship and loyalty are more precious than riches.'

BADGERS

Badgers have always felt the call of the fortress of Salamandastron, fulfilling a destiny which is carved on its stones. As rulers of the fortress, they are great warriors of immense strength, within whose souls dark and light battle for supremacy. The curse of the badger warrior is the fabled Bloodwrath, which is able to make a badger utterly disregard his own life in an attempt to destroy his enemy. Hugely loyal, the rulers of Salamandastron frequently come to the aid of the Redwallers.

The wisdom inherent in badgers stands the females in good stead for their traditional role as guardian mothers of Redwall Abbey.

HARES

Whether actors, travellers or members of the Long Patrol, the hares of Redwall are unforgettable characters. With their elaborate formality of speech and dress, their singing, constant chatter and huge appetites, they are a much loved part of Redwall lore.

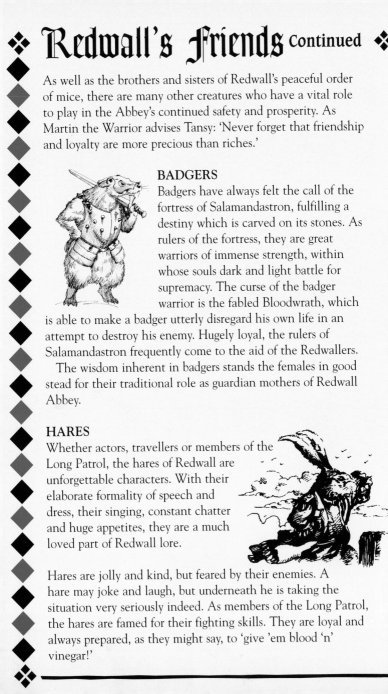

Hares are jolly and kind, but feared by their enemies. A hare may joke and laugh, but underneath he is taking the situation very seriously indeed. As members of the Long Patrol, the hares are famed for their fighting skills. They are loyal and always prepared, as they might say, to 'give 'em blood 'n' vinegar!'

HEDGEHOGS

Hedgehogs are, for the most part, sensible and kind beasts. At Redwall they are usually the cellar keepers and proud of their fine concoctions. As well as the cellar hogs, there is also the young hedgehog maid, Tansy, whose wisdom and judgement ensure that she becomes the first hedgehog to be made Abbess of Redwall. We also meet the famous Dunehogs, whose displays of Spinetussling entertained Martin, and the brave Waterhogs of *The Long Patrol*.

MOLES

Homely and sensible, moles have played an important role at Redwall ever since the Abbey was first designed. It was moles who first dug the Abbey foundations (at which point the tradition of calling the chief Redwall mole 'Foremole' began). The technical know-how of the moles and their ability to tunnel have come to the aid of the Redwallers on many occasions. It was moles who dug the tunnels and flooded Kotir; moles who solved the mechanism leading to Martin's tomb; moles who dug the underground tunnels which foiled General Ironbeak; and moles who worked out a way to move the Abbey's foundation stone.

Moles are renowned for their logic and 'molesense', but detest water and heights. They love good food, with their all-time-favourite being deeper 'n' ever turnip 'n' tater 'n' beetroot pie. They are also fond of singing in their unique style - with a paw over one ear - although their companions do not always appreciate it!

OTTERS

Otters are boisterous, brave and really passionate about one thing - hotroot soup. Although they do not usually inhabit the Abbey, they are frequent visitors and make up guard patrols in times of danger. The leader of the otters is always given the same title - Skipper.

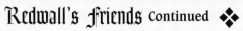

Otters are skilled warriors, fighting with sling and stones, javelin or bow and arrow, and they are able to vanish into the water at a moment's notice. They are also excellent craftsbeasts, making furniture - such as a desk for Abbess Germaine. Although often seen as reckless, otters are also hugely valiant creatures, many of them giving their lives in the name of freedom.

SHREWS

Although their argumentative natures can sometimes give the impression of chaotic discord, the Guosim - Guerrilla Union of Shrews in Mossflower - live by a strict code of rules and laws. The title of the Guosim leader - Log a Log - is passed down through the generations and derives from the call for the ferryshrew to take other creatures across the river. Given their tendency to all speak at once, shrew law dictates that only the individual holding the black stone may speak at any one time.

The Guosim are fierce warriors, fighting with short rapiers and travelling the waterways in logboats. They are passionate about fighting for freedom, and rarely take prisoners. Shrews are excellent cooks, particularly partial to a bit of meadowcream, and produce such specialities as shrewbeer.

SQUIRRELS

The squirrels have always had
an important role to
play in Redwall history.
From Ranguvar
Foeseeker's great support of
Luke in his battle against
Vilu Daskar, they have
fought bravely for Redwall and
all that it stands for. Beyond Redwall, too, squirrels of great
bravery have been associated with the Abbey. The great
Russa Nodrey helps Tammo to join the Long Patrol. She also
saves the life of the young Russano the Wise.

Squirrels played an important part in the building of the
Abbey. With their legendary climbing skills, they were the
ideal creatures to put up the scaffolding during its
construction. They are skilled and brave fighters who make
full use of their detailed knowledge of the treetops for the
purpose of attack or surveillance.

BIRDS

Redwall has a great number of loyal feathered friends who are
often crucial to the success of a Redwall mission and are
ready to lend a wing. Of special significance to the Abbey is
Warbeak the Sparra Queen,
who helps
Matthias to look
for the sword of
Martin the Warrior.
She and Martin become
great friends as she risks her life
to help the young mouse. Warbeak comes to the aid of the
Redwallers again when she offers to seek out the travelling
Matthias and give him a vital map. Warbeak is tragically
killed in the attempt. Her life is celebrated as that of a true
friend of Redwall.

❖ Redwall Testers ❖

Test your knowledge of the whole Redwall series with these challenging and intriguing puzzles, but don't worry if you get stuck, the answers are at the back of this booklet.

FRIEND OR FOE

Redwallers know the value of anagrams in concealing a secret until it is time for it to be known. Decipher the names below and say whether the characters are Redwall's friend or foe.

1. Yakle (Martin the Warrior)
2. Raabgo Wullwray (Legend of Luke)
3. Fingrag (Legend of Luke)
4. Hitraw (Outcast of Redwall)
5. Songcaru (Salamandastron)
6. Udesasom (Redwall)
7. Wolf Rocner (Redwall)
8. Laidtip (Mattimeo)
9. Drisk Ralluf (Pearls of Lutra)
10. Mord Rigorjape (Long Patrol)

AYE, AYE, CAP'N!

From triremes to logboats, skiffs to rafts, Redwallers and their foes are no strangers to life on the high seas. Can you match the name of a captain from the list on the left to the name of his ship on the right?

CAPTAIN	SHIP
TRAMUN CLOGG	ABBOT BERNARD
RIPFANG	NIGHTWAKE
FINNBARR GALEDEEP	CRABCLAW
DURRY QUILL	GREENHAWK
VILU DASKAR	FREEBOOTER
WARPCLAW	WAVEWORM
GRIMTOOTH	BLACKSAIL
FLOGGA	GUTPROW
RIPTUNG	SEASCARAB
ROMSCA	BLOODWAKE
BARRANCA	PEARL QUEEN
HOOKFIN	GABRIEL
DANDIN	WAVEBLADE
ORGEYE	GORELEECH
REYNARD CHOPSNOUT	RATHELM

The Redwall Quiz

With questions covering every one of the tales, put your Redwall knowledge to the ultimate test in this great Redwall quiz.

1. Name the four rabbits who make up the Mirdop.

2. Gonff the Mousethief's parents are killed by Verdauga Greeneyes during a short-lived rebellion in Mossflower. Who brought him up?

3. What does Mask call himself when disguised as a fox?

4. Name Swartt Sixclaw's wife.

5. What relation is Lord Rawnblade of Salamandastron to Sunflash the Mace?

6. What type of animal are Urgan Nagru's Dirgecallers?

7. Name the discovery, made by Arula, that makes Salamandastron invulnerable to siege.

8. What name do the Guosim give to Asmodeus?

9. Which herb always makes Basil sneeze?

10. Which two Redwallers share the unofficial title of Abbey beekeeper?

11. Who makes the flag that the Redwallers take into battle with them against the Rapscallions?

12. What was Soll's name before tragedy befell his family?

13. What kind of animal is the Gloomer?

14. What was Egbert the Scholar's mole name?

15. Name the *Goreleech's* slavemaster.

16. On which forepaw, left or right, does Veil, like his father, have six claws?

17. TRAG member Tan Loc has sworn vengeance on one searat in particular. Who?

18. What is the name of the army trained by Felldoh to attack Marshank?

19. What is Thrugg given for bringing the Icetor flowers back to Redwall?

20. Name the sparrow who stole Martin the Warrior's sword from the weathervane.

21. What caused Loamhedge Abbey to sink beneath the earth?

22. What skill is Rasconza well known for?

23. Name the squirrel prisoner whom Midge and Tammo help to escape from the Rapscallions.

24. In ancient squirrel language, who was the Reguba?